THE FIRE PLUME

The Fire Plume

Legends of the American Indians

COLLECTED BY HENRY ROWE SCHOOLCRAFT

EDITED BY JOHN BIERHORST

PICTURES BY ALAN E. COBER

THE DIAL PRESS, INC./NEW YORK

Contents

FOREWORD

During the long winter evenings, when work was light, tales like these were heard around the Indian lodge fire. Many of them undoubtedly served to reinforce ancient beliefs or to preserve bits of tribal history. Some were intended as lessons for children. Others were purely for amusement.

Unfortunately European settlers of the seventeenth and eighteenth centuries took little notice of this tradition. Not until the early nineteenth century did a widespread interest in Indian culture, and Indian legends, really develop. By that time much valuable material had, in all probability, been lost forever, especially that which belonged to the great Algonquin family of tribes, who once occupied most of the northeastern United States and adjoining Canada.

It is from this family of tribes—including the Chippewa, Shawnee, Ottawa, and Menominee—

that the legends in this book were taken. They were collected by the explorer Henry Rowe Schoolcraft (1793–1864) during his travels through the upper Mississippi valley and Great Lakes region, where Algonquin tribes still lived or where they had fled from settled areas in the east. Many of Schoolcraft's tales were passed on to him by literate frontiersmen who were able to translate the original languages. Others he undoubtedly heard from his wife, who was half Chippewa, or from members of her family.

In the 1820's and 30's Schoolcraft frequently served as superintendent of Indian affairs in the territory around Lake Michigan and Lake Superior. Eventually he mastered the Chippewa language, and by 1850 he had become a recognized authority on Indian lore. Drawing upon this extensive knowledge, he was able to fill out his stories with details that made them more readily understandable to readers of English.

Today when students of Indian culture record

legends, they attempt to make an exact translation. Schoolcraft did not merely translate, he interpreted. The result is a story form that is loosely knit, often poetic, highly romantic—and thoroughly American.

Peboan and Seegwun

An old man was sitting alone in his lodge by the side of a frozen stream. It was the close of winter and his fire was almost out. He appeared very old and very desolate. His locks were white with age. He trembled in every joint. Day after day passed in solitude, and he heard nothing but the sound of the wind, sweeping before it the new-fallen snow.

One day, as his fire was just dying, a handsome young man approached and entered his dwelling. His cheeks were red with the blood of youth, his eyes sparkled, and a smile was on his lips. He walked with a light, quick step. His forehead was bound with a wreath of sweet grass, in place of a warrior's frontlet, and in his hand he carried a bunch of flowers.

"Ah, my son," said the old man, "I am happy to see you. Come in. Come, tell me of your adventures and what strange lands you have been to see. Let us pass the night together. I will tell you of my prowess and what deeds I can perform. You shall do the same, and we will amuse ourselves."

He then drew from his sack a curiously wrought antique pipe, and having filled it with tobacco, handed it to his guest. When this ceremony was concluded they began to speak.

"I blow my breath," said the old man, "and the

streams stand still. The water becomes as hard as clear stone."

"I breathe," said the young man, "and flowers spring up all over the plains."

"I shake my locks," retorted the old man, "and snow covers the land. The leaves fall from the trees at my command, and my breath blows them away. The birds get up from the water and fly to a distant land. The animals hide themselves from my breath, and the very ground becomes as hard as flint."

"I shake my ringlets," rejoined the young man, "and warm showers of soft rain fall upon the earth. My voice recalls the birds. The warmth of my breath unlocks the streams. Plants lift up their heads out of the earth. Music fills the forest wherever I walk, and all nature rejoices."

At length the sun began to rise. A gentle warmth came over the place. The tongue of the old man became silent. The robin and the bluebird began to sing on the top of the lodge. The stream began to murmur by the door, and the fragrance of growing herbs and flowers came softly on the spring breeze.

Daylight fully revealed to the young man the appearance of his host. When he looked upon him, he had the icy visage of Peboan. Streams began to flow from his eyes. As the sun increased, he grew smaller and smaller, and soon had melted completely away. Where his lodge fire had been, nothing remained but the miskodeed, a small white flower with a pink border, which is one of the first to bloom in the northern forest.

The Red Swan

Odjibwa, the youngest of three brothers, was out hunting one day, when he caught sight of a bear. According to a family agreement, the bear was not his to kill. It was reserved for his older, more experienced brothers. Hesitating for a moment, as if to test his own daring, he found that he felt no fear within his breast, but rather a surge of defiance. Boldly he claimed the bear for himself, and taking careful aim, with a sure and steady arm, felled it with one shot.

Suddenly, just as the bear was hit, a reddish glow brightened the surrounding air. Odjibwa rubbed his eyes, thinking it must be an illusion. But the red glow persisted. Off in the distance he heard a sound like a human voice, yet strangely different from any voice he had ever heard before. He stopped to listen. Again he heard it and felt it calling to him. So strongly did it lure him that in his eagerness to follow it he forgot the bear he had slain only a few moments before. Pushing ahead through the brush, he came out on the shore of a small lake—and saw immediately the object that had attracted him.

There in the water sat a magnificent red swan, its plumage glittering in the sun. Now and again it made the same curious sound he had heard before. He was within bowshot, and pulling the arrow from the bowstring up to his ear, he took his aim. But the arrow missed. Again and again he shot, till his quiver was empty. Undisturbed, the swan moved around in circles, stretching its long neck and dipping its bill into the water.

Odjibwa ran home and got all his own and his brothers' arrows, and shot them all away. He then stood and gazed at the beautiful bird. Suddenly he remembered his brothers saying that in their deceased father's medicine sack were three magic arrows. Off he started without hesitation, so great was his desire to have the swan. At any other time he would have considered it a sacrilege to open his father's sack. Neither of his brothers would have dared to do so. But now he hastily seized the three arrows and ran back, leaving the other contents scattered over the lodge.

The swan was still there. With great precision he shot the first arrow, and came very near the mark. The second came even closer. As he took the last arrow, he felt his arm grow firmer. Drawing it back with all his strength, he let it go and saw it pass through the neck of the swan a little above the breast. Still the bird did not appear injured. It waited a few moments, then slowly began to flap its wings. Gradually it rose into the air, flying off toward the sinking of the sun.

Odjibwa started after it, running as fast as he could. As he rounded the lake, he spied several of the arrows he had shot from the opposite shore. Hastily he retrieved them and continued on. So great was his speed that he would shoot an arrow, catch up to it, and even pass it. Through deep woods, past lakes and streams, down valleys and over prairies he ran, toward the red sky in the west. Just before nightfall, after taking one last run, he began looking about for a place to rest. I can run fast, he thought, and tomorrow when the sun has risen I will sooner or later catch up to the swan. Emerging from the forest, he found himself in a large clearing. Farther

on were lodges and the sounds of men chopping wood.

Tired though he was, and in need of refreshment, the thought of the swan remained uppermost in his mind as he made his way toward the village. Drawing near, he heard the voice of the watchman crying, "We are visited!" He advanced, and the watchman directed him to the lodge of the chief. "It is there you must go in," he said, and left him.

"Come in, come in, take a seat," said the chief, pointing to the side where his daughter sat. "It is there you must sit."

They gave him food, and since he was a stranger, asked him but few questions, waiting for him to speak first. After dark the chief said to his daughter, "Take our son-in-law's moccasins and see if they be torn. If so, mend them for him, and bring in his bundle." Odjibwa thought it strange that he should be so warmly received, and given a wife so soon, without his wishing it. It was some time, however, before she would take his moccasins. It displeased him to see her so reluctant, and when she did fetch them, he snatched them out of her hand and hung them up himself. He lay down and thought of the swan, and made up his mind to be off by dawn.

He awoke early, and spoke to the young woman, but she gave no answer. He touched her lightly. "What do you want?" she asked, and she turned her back toward him. "Tell me what time the swan passed. I am following it. Come out and point the direction."

"Do you think you can catch up to it?" she said. "You are foolish." Nonetheless she went out and pointed the direction she thought he should go.

Odjibwa set out slowly. When the sun had risen, he began to travel at his usual speed. He spent the day running, and when night came he was unexpectedly pleased to find himself near another village. Again he heard a watchman crying out, "We are visited!" and soon the men of the village came out to see the stranger. He was again told to enter the lodge of the chief, and his reception was in every respect the same as the previous night, only that the young woman was more beautiful and received him very kindly. Although he was urged to stay, his mind remained fixed on the object of his journey. Before daylight he asked the young woman what time the red swan had passed and to point out the way. She did, saying that it had passed the day before when the sun was between midday and *pung-ishemoo*, its falling place.

Again he set out slowly, but when the sun had risen, he tried his speed by shooting an arrow ahead and catching up to it. On and on he ran until, toward nightfall, he came to a small low lodge. There was a light within. As he approached he could see an old man sitting alone, warming his back at the fire. "Come in, my grandchild, and take a seat," he said. "Remove your things and dry them, for you must be fatigued, and I will prepare you something to eat."

Odjibwa did as he was requested. When he had eaten, he leaned back and listened as the host began to speak:

"Young man, the errand you are on is very difficult. Many young men have passed with the same purpose, but none have returned.

"The red swan you are following belongs to a certain magician, who has sent her out over the earth in search of a young man of courage and great daring. A deep sadness, bringing shame and dishonor, has fallen upon him, and he seeks a deliverer to put an end to his suffering.

"It is well known in our land that the magician's power resides in a marvelous cap made entirely of wampum, which in former times he wore firmly attached to his scalp. But one day a party of warriors sent by an envious chief caught him off guard, snatched the scalp, and made away with it, leaving his head bare and bloodied. Several years have passed and still his head has not healed. Meanwhile the warriors go dancing from village to village, displaying their trophy, calling insults upon it, and boasting of their own prowess. With every insult it receives, the magician groans with pain. Many a young man such as yourself has been enticed by the red swan in order to rescue the wampum scalp. Whoever is fortunate enough to succeed will receive the red swan herself as his reward.

"In the morning you will proceed on your way, and toward evening you will come to the magician's lodge. You have been chosen for your skill and your daring. Never swerving in your determination, you have followed the swan faithfully, resisting the temptations offered you by hosts along the way. Go forward, my son. Your heart is strong. I have a presentiment you will succeed."

"I will try," said Odjibwa, and early the next

morning he started off. Toward evening he came to the lodge, just as he had been told, and heard the groans of the magician. Upon entering he was immediately made welcome. "You have traveled far," said the magician. "You must rest and take something to eat." Removing his leggings and moccasins, Odjibwa sat down beside the fire and looked around him. Strewn about the lodge were heavy furs, robes, brilliant feathers, strands of wampum and other riches—yet no sign of life save the magician himself, whose head still appeared bloodied from the loss of his scalp. On one side, however, Odjibwa could see that the lodge was partitioned, and every now and then he heard a rustling noise.

After he had taken some food, the old magician began to tell him about the lost scalp—how a band of warriors had stolen it, how they dishonored it and brought him great suffering. Then he told of the numerous unsuccessful attempts to regain it. When he had finished, Odjibwa lay down before the fire on a bed of robes that had been prepared for his use. In the solemn quiet of the dimly lit lodge he gathered his thoughts and imagined the perils of the task that lay ahead of him. As he slept, he dreamed; and in his dream a hawk rose up from the forest. It circled in the air. Again it circled, and again and again.

When he awoke, the magician was standing over him, ready to hand him his things and send him on his way. The sun had not yet risen. Without delay he made his preparations, and soon he was off on his dangerous adventure. The path he took was remote from the lodgings of men. Not a soul did he encounter along the way. But toward the end of the day—about the time that the sun hangs toward home—he heard the shouts of a great many people off in the distance. Looking ahead, he could see a clearing and several men. The closer he came, the more he saw. Still more came into view as he approached the opening, and as he emerged from the trees their heads appeared as numerous as the hanging leaves. Tense with excitement, he made his way among them. Farther ahead, in the midst of the crowd, he could see a post and something waving on it—the scalp.

Off and on the air was filled with the sound of chanting as they danced around the post. The rush and hum of so many people was like the beating of waves after a storm. Suddenly, in the heat of the throng, he felt a quickening pulse in his arms. His body rose up. Transformed into a hawk, he soared past the heads of the warriors, causing them to jump aside in alarm. Then, with a terrifying scream, he swooped down on the scalp and tore it loose with his talons. The moment they saw what had taken place, they filled the air with their cries. "It is taken from us! It is taken from us!" Immediately they set out in pursuit, but Odjibwa soared high above them and soon disappeared over the trees.

Hearing the scream of the hawk, the magician

stepped out of his lodge and began searching the sky for some sign of the young man's return. Soon Odjibwa appeared, and within a matter of moments he stood before his host, changed back to his usual form, holding the wampum scalp in his hands. With tremendous force he brought it down on the magician's head, dealing him a blow so severe that the old man's limbs shot out and quivered in agony. He sank to the ground and remained motionless for a long time—so long that it seemed he would not revive. At last he showed signs of life. His body stirred, he sat up. As he rose to his feet, Odjibwa beheld not an aged man but one of the handsomest young men he had ever seen.

"Thank you, my friend," he said. "You see that your kindness and bravery have restored me to my former self. It was so ordained, and you have accomplished the victory."

Together they entered the lodge. The young magician urged Odjibwa to remain as his guest, and they soon established a warm friendship. Time elapsed, but still the magician did not speak of the red swan, nor was there any visible sign of her presence in the room where they sat. At last the moment arrived for Odjibwa to make preparations for his return. The magician repaid him for his kindness and bravery with gifts of wampum, robes, and all such things as would make him an influential man. But though his curiosity about the red swan was at its height, he controlled his feelings. On this subject he felt it would be improper to speak his mind, since the one he had rendered such a service to, whose hospitality he was now enjoying, and who had richly rewarded him, had never so much as mentioned it.

His traveling pack was ready, and he was taking his leave, when the young magician at last spoke:

"Friend, I know why it is that you have come so far. You have accomplished your mission and conferred a lasting obligation upon me. Your perse-

verance shall not go unrewarded, and if you under-
take other things in the same spirit as this, you will
always succeed. Though I would be happy to go
with you, it is my duty to remain here. I have
given you all you will need as long as you live.
Your reluctance to speak of the red swan is most
fitting. Yet I vowed that whoever rescued my scalp
should possess her."

He then knocked on the partition. A door opened
and the Red Swan appeared. She was a handsome
young woman, and as she stood majestically before
him it would be impossible to describe her beauty,
for she looked as if she did not belong on earth.

"Take her," the magician said. "She is my sister,
treat her well, she is worthy of you. What you have
done for me merits even more. She is ready to go
with you to your kindred and friends, and has been
so ever since your arrival. My good wishes go with
you both."

The Red Swan looked upon her husband with

admiration as he bid farewell to his friend. Together, bound by mutual trust and the promise of
deep affection, they began the long journey home.

The White Stone Canoe

There was once a very beautiful young girl, who died suddenly on the day she was to have been married to a handsome young man. He was also brave, but his heart was not strong enough to endure this loss. From the hour she was buried, there was no more joy or peace for him. He would often visit the spot where the women had buried her and sit there dreaming.

Some of his friends thought he should try to forget his sorrow by hunting or by following the warpath. But war and hunting had lost their charms for him. His heart was already dead within him. He pushed aside both his war club and his bow and arrows.

He had heard the old people say there was a path that led to the land of souls, and he made up his mind to follow it. One morning, after having made his preparations for the journey, he picked up his bow and arrows, called to his dog, and started out. He hardly knew which way to go. He was only guided by the tradition that he must go south. As he walked along, he could see at first no change in the face of the country. Forests and hills and valleys and streams had the same look which they wore in his native place. There was snow on the ground, and sometimes it was even piled and matted on the thick trees and bushes. But after a long while it began to diminish, and finally disappeared. The forest took on a more cheerful appearance, the leaves put forth their buds, and before he was aware of the completeness of the change, he found himself surrounded by spring.

He had left behind him the land of snow and ice. The clouds of winter had rolled away from the sky. The air became mild. A pure field of blue was above him. As he went along he saw flowers beside his path and heard the songs of birds. By these signs he knew that he was going the right way, for they agreed with the traditions of his tribe.

At length he spied a path. It led him through a grove, then up a long, high ridge, on the very top of which there stood a lodge. At the door was an old man with white hair, whose eyes, though deeply sunken, had a fiery brilliance. He had a long robe of skins thrown loosely around his shoulders and a staff in his hands.

The young man began to tell his story. But the old chief stopped him before he had spoken ten words. "I have expected you," he said, "and had just risen to welcome you to my lodge. She whom you seek passed here only a few days ago, and being tired from her journey, rested herself here. Enter my lodge and be seated. I will then answer your questions and give you directions for the remainder of your journey."

When this was accomplished, the old chief brought the young man back out through the door of the lodge. "You see yonder lake," said he, "and the wide-stretching blue plains beyond. It is the land of souls. You now stand upon its borders, and my lodge is at the gate of entrance. But you cannot take your body along. Leave it here with your bow and arrows and your dog. You will find them safe on your return."

So saying, he went back into the lodge, and the traveler bounded forward, as if his feet had suddenly been given the power of wings. But all things retained their natural colors and shapes. The woods and leaves, the streams and lakes, were only brighter and more beautiful than before. Animals bounded across his path with a freedom and confidence that seemed to tell him there was no bloodshed here. Birds of beautiful plumage lived in the groves and sported in the waters.

There was one thing, however, that struck him as peculiar. He noticed that he was not stopped by trees or other objects. He seemed to walk directly through them. They were, in fact, merely the souls or shadows of real trees. He became aware that he was in a land of shadows.

When he had traveled half a day's journey, through a country which grew more and more attractive, he came to the banks of a broad lake, in the center of which was a large and beautiful island. He found a canoe of shining white stone tied to the shore. He was now sure that he had followed the right path, for the aged man had told him of this. There were also shining paddles. He immediately got into the canoe, and had just taken the paddles in his hands when, to his joy and surprise, he beheld the object of his search in another canoe, exactly like his own in every respect. She had exactly imitated his motions, and they were side by side.

At once they pushed out from the shore and began to cross the lake. Its waves seemed to be rising, and at a distance looked ready to swallow them up. But just as they came to the whitened edge of the first great wave, it seemed to melt away, as if it had been merely a shadow or a reflection. No sooner did they pass through one wreath of foam, however, than another still more threatening rose up. They were in constant fear. Moreover, through the clear water they could see the bones of many men who had perished, strewn on the bottom of the lake.

The Master of Life had decreed that the two of them should pass safely through, for they had both

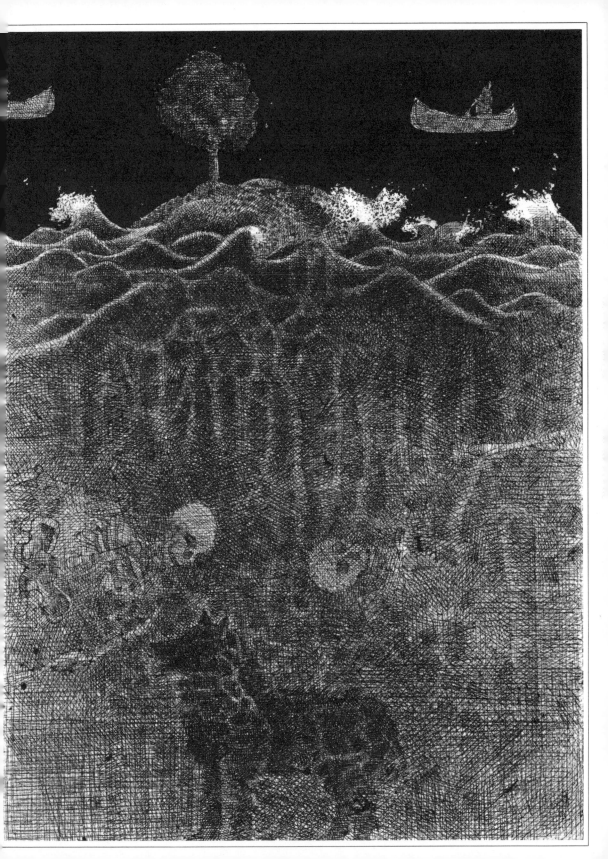

led good lives on earth. But they saw many others struggling and sinking in the waves. There were old men and young men, and women too. Some passed safely through, and some sank. But it was only the little children whose canoes seemed to meet no waves at all. Finally every difficulty was passed, as if in an instant, and they both leaped out on the happy island.

They felt that the air was food. It strengthened and nourished them. They wandered over the blissful fields, where everything was made to please the eye and the ear. There were no storms. There was no ice, no chilly wind. No one shivered for want of warm clothes. No one suffered from hunger, no one mourned the dead. They saw no graves. They heard of no wars. There was no hunting for animals, for the air itself was food.

Gladly would the young warrior have remained there forever, but he was obliged to go back for his body. He did not see the Master of Life, but he heard his voice in a soft breeze. "Go back," said the voice, "to the land where you came from. Your time has not yet come. The duties for which I made you, and which you are to perform, are not yet finished. Return to your people and accomplish the duties of a good man. You will be the ruler of your tribe for many days. The rules you must observe will be told you by my messenger who keeps the gate. When he gives you back your body, he will tell you what to do. Listen to him, and you shall one day rejoin the spirit whom you must now leave behind. She has been accepted, and will be here always, as young and as happy as she was when I first called her from the land of snows."

When the voice had ceased, the young man awoke. It had been only a dream, and he was still in the bitter land of snows, and hunger, and tears.

Three Chippewa Fables

I. THE GROUNDHOG FAMILY

One long winter, a female groundhog with a numerous family of young ones was burrowing in her wauzh, or hole in the ground. Every day she would go out and get roots and other things, which she brought in for the young ones to eat. They were impatient for spring, but she told them to lie close and keep warm, and never to venture toward the mouth of the wauzh.

At last they grew very impatient to see the light and the green woods, and said, "Mother, is it not almost spring?"

"No! no!" said she, in a cross humor. "Keep still and wait patiently. It hails, it snows, it is cold, it is windy. Why should you wish to go out?"

This she told them so often, and in such a bad temper, that they at last suspected some deception. One day she came in after having been gone a long while and fell asleep, with her mouth open. The little ones peeped in slyly and saw on her teeth the remains of the nice white bulbous roots of the mo-na-wing, or adder's-tongue violet. They at once knew it was spring, and without disturbing the old one, who only wanted to keep them in till they were full-grown, away they scampered out of the hole and dispersed themselves about the forest. And so the family were all scattered.

II. THE THREE CRANBERRIES

Three cranberries were living in a lodge together. One was green, one white, and one red. They were sisters. There was snow on the ground; and as the men were absent, they felt afraid, and began to say to each other, "What shall we do if the wolves come?"

"I," said the green one, "will climb up a shingoub tree."

"I," said the white one, "will hide myself in the kettle of boiled hominy."

"And I," said the red one, "will conceal myself under the snow."

Presently the wolves came, and each one did as

she had said. But only one of the three had judged wisely. The wolves immediately ran to the kettle and ate up the hominy, and with it the white cranberry. The red one was trampled to pieces by their feet, and her blood spotted the snow. But she who had climbed the thick spruce tree escaped notice, and was saved.

III. THE RACCOON AND THE CRAWFISH

As long as anyone can remember, the raccoon has searched for the crawfish along the margins of streams. There was once a time, however, when the enmity between the two species grew so great, and the consequent wariness for each other was such, that the poor raccoon, with all his stealthiness, was at last put to great straits for a meal. The crawfish would no longer venture near the shore, and the raccoon was on the point of starvation. At

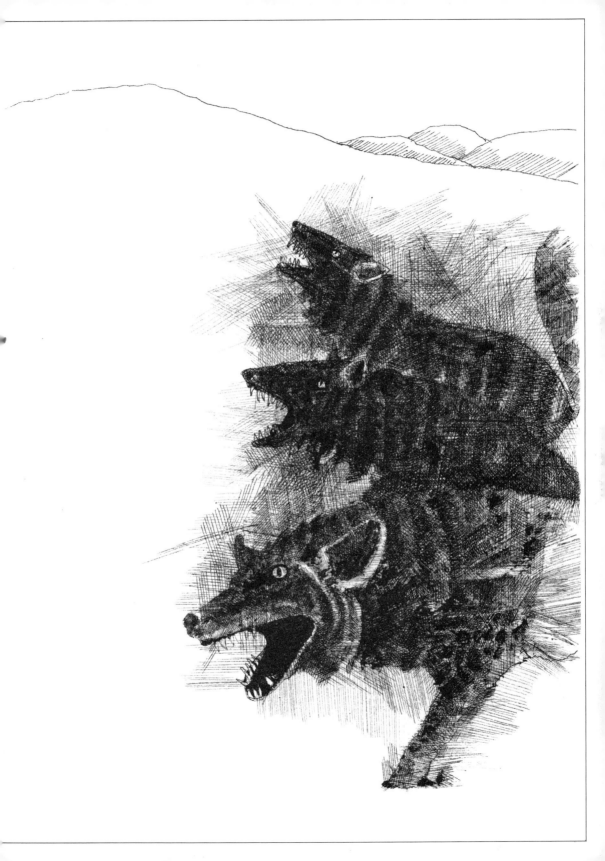

length he thought of a way to decoy his prey.

Knowing that crawfish feed on worms, he got together a quantity of old rotten wood, filled with worms, and stuffing it in his mouth and ears and powdering it over his body, he lay down by the water's edge.

Soon an old crawfish came warily out from the water and crawled all over and around his apparently dead enemy. He rejoiced to find an end put to the raccoon's murderous ways, and cried out to the others, "Come up my sisters and brothers, Aissibun is dead, come up and eat him."

But when they had all gathered around, the raccoon suddenly sprang up and set to killing and devouring them so quickly that not one was left alive.

While he was still rummaging through the broken limbs, a little female crawfish, carrying her infant sister on her back, came up, looking for her relatives. Finding they had all been eaten by the raccoon, she resolved not to survive the destruction of her kindred. Boldly she went up to the enemy and said, "Here, Aissibun, you see me and my little sister. We are all alone. You have eaten up our parents and all our friends. Eat us too."

The raccoon felt reproached by this act of courage. "No," said he. "I have banqueted on the largest and the fattest. I will not dishonor myself by such little prey."

At that moment Manabozho appeared. "Shame on thee, Aissibun," he said. "Thou art a devil and a merciless thief. Get thee hence, lest I change thee into a lowly fish!"

Then he took up the little crawfish and her infant sister and cast them into the stream. "There you may dwell," said he. "Hide yourselves under the stones, and hereafter you shall be playthings for little children."

Wawanosh

Wawanosh was the head of an ancient family of his tribe, which had preserved the line of chieftainship unbroken from a remote time. To the reputation of birth he added the advantages of a tall and commanding person and the impressive qualities of strength and courage. His bow was noted for its size and the feats he had performed with it. His counsel was sought as much as his strength was feared, so that he had come to be equally regarded as a hunter, a warrior, and a counselor. He had now passed the prime of his days, and the term *akkee waizee,* meaning one who has been long on the earth, was applied to him.

Wawanosh had an only daughter, a handsome young woman who had lived through eighteen springs. Her father was not more celebrated for his deeds of strength than she for her slender grace, her dark eyes, and dark flowing hair. Many were the young men who sought her hand, but only one had found favor. He was a young hunter of humble parentage, who had no merits to recommend him other than a tall, straight frame, a manly step, and a youthful face beaming with love. The daughter longed to return his love, but the father remained unmoved. Wawanosh sought an alliance more suitable to the rank and high pretensions of his family.

"Listen to me, young man," he replied to the trembling hunter, who had come to seek his approval, "and be attentive to my words."

"You ask me to bestow upon you my daughter, the chief comfort of my age, and my choicest gift from the Master of Life. Others have asked of me this boon who were as young and as eager. Many have had better claims to become my son-in-law. Have you considered the deeds which have raised me in authority and made my name known to the enemies of my nation? Where is there a chief who is not proud to be the friend of Wawanosh? Where is there a hunter who has excelled Wawanosh? Where is there a warrior who has taken an equal number of scalps? Have you not heard that my fathers came from the east, bearing the marks of chieftaincy?

"Think not that my warrior blood shall mingle with yours. None but the brave can ever hope to claim an alliance with the family of Wawanosh. Go, then, young man, and earn a name for yourself."

The intimidated young hunter departed. He was determined to do a deed that would make him worthy of the daughter of Wawanosh, or die in the attempt. He called together a number of his young companions and told them of his plan to lead an expedition against the enemy, and asked for their assistance. Several of them took to the idea immediately, the others were soon persuaded, and before ten suns had set he found himself at the head of a formidable party of young warriors. Like himself, all were eager to distinguish themselves in battle.

Each warrior was armed with a bow and a quiver of arrows tipped with flint or jasper. Each carried a sack filled with pounded corn mixed with pemmican or maple sugar. All were provided with war clubs of hard wood, fastened to belts of deerskin. In addition to knives of stone or copper, some carried the ancient *shemagun*, a long pole with a spearhead of flint firmly tied on with deer's sinews. Adorned with feathers, their bodies painted, they gathered together for the war dance.

Their leader was distinguished by the feathers of the bald eagle. As he led them around a bright fire of pine wood he chanted.

> Hear my voice, birds of war!
> I prepare a feast for you to feed on;
> I see you cross the enemy's lines;
> Like you I shall go.
> I wish the swiftness of your wings,
> I wish the vengeance of your claws.
> I muster my friends,
> I follow your flight.
> Come, you young men warriors,
> Bear your anger to the place of fighting!

Then, suddenly halting, they raised the war cry, and the dance immediately began. An old man, sitting at the head of the ring, beat time upon a drum, while several of the older warriors shook rattles and made the woods echo with their song.

> Here on my breast have I bled!
> See! My battle scars!
> Mountains tremble at my yell!
> I strike for life.

The dance continued, with short pauses, for two successive days and nights. Often during a pause the medicine man, who led the ceremony, would address them with words of encouragement. Then the dance would begin again, with renewed vigor. Again the young men would chant.

> From the south they come,
> The birds, the warlike birds,
>   with sounding wings.
>
> I wish to change myself
> To the body of that swift bird.
>
> I throw away my body in the strife.

At length the medicine man uttered his final prediction of success. One by one the warriors dropped away from the fire, each making his way to the appointed meeting place at the edge of the enemy's country. Their leader was soon to join them, but not until he had sought out the daughter of Wawanosh. He warned her of his determination never to return unless he could establish his name as a warrior. He told her of the humiliation he had suffered at the harsh words of her father. Never could he be content, with or without her, until he had proved his courage to the entire tribe. Again he told her of his great attachment to her. She, too, pledged her love, and they parted.

After this last meeting the only news she was ever to receive from her lover was brought to her by one of his warriors, who reported that he had distinguished himself by the most heroic bravery, but at the end of the battle he had been shot through the breast. The wound had been beyond the power of the young warriors to cure. They had carried him a day's journey toward home, when, greatly weakened, he had finally died in their arms.

From that moment on there was no more happiness for the daughter of Wawanosh. Refusing to take food, she passed her days and nights in solitude, often withdrawing to a lonely spot in the forest where she would sit beneath the boughs of a tree for hours at a time.

It was not long before a small bird of beautiful plumage flew into the tree under which she usually sat. It was a strange bird, such as had never been seen before. Every day it came and sang, remaining until dark. Her imagination soon led her to suppose that it was the spirit of her lover, and her visits to the forest became more frequent. Still she fasted, growing weaker with each passing day, until the death she so eagerly desired finally came to her relief. After her death the bird was never seen again, and it became widely believed that this mysterious

creature had flown away with her spirit.

But bitter tears of regret fell in the lodge of Wawanosh. Too late he regretted his false pride and his harsh treatment of the noble youth.

The Broken Wing

There were six young falcons living in a nest, all but one of whom were still unable to fly, when it happened that both the parent birds were shot by hunters in one day. The young brood waited with impatience for their return. But night came and they were left without parents and without food.

Gray Eagle, the eldest and the only one whose feathers had become stout enough to enable him to leave the nest, assumed the duty of stilling their cries and providing them with food. But after a short time had passed, he, by an unlucky accident, got one of his wings broken in pouncing on a swan. This was especially unlucky because the season had arrived when they were soon to go south for the winter, and they were only waiting to become a little stronger and a little more agile before setting out on the journey. When Gray Eagle did not return, they decided to go in search of him, and found him sorely wounded and unable to fly.

"Brothers," he said, "an accident has befallen me. But do not let this prevent your going to a warmer climate. Winter is rapidly approaching, and you cannot remain here. It is better that I alone should die than for all of you to suffer miserably on my account."

"No! no!" they replied with one voice. "We will

not forsake you. We will share your sufferings. We will abandon our journey and take care of you, as you did of us, before we were able to take care of ourselves. If the climate kills you, it shall kill us. Do you think we can so soon forget your brotherly care, which has surpassed a father's, and even a mother's kindness? Whether you live or die, we will share your fate."

They sought out a hollow tree, carried their wounded nestmate there, and before the rigors of winter set in, they stored up enough food to carry them through. To make sure it would last, two of them went south, leaving the other three to feed and protect their older brother.

In due time Gray Eagle recovered from his wound, and he repaid their kindness by giving them instruction in the art of hunting. As spring advanced, they began to venture out of their hiding place and were all successful in getting food to eke out their winter's stock, except the youngest, who was called

Peepi-geewi-zains, or Pigeon Hawk. Being small and foolish, flying hither and yon, he always came back without anything. At last Gray Eagle spoke to him and demanded the cause of his ill luck.

"It is not my smallness or weakness," said Peepi-geewi-zains, "that prevents me from bringing home food as well as my brothers. I kill ducks and other birds every time I go out. But just as I get to the woods, a large owl robs me of my prey."

"Don't despair, brother," said Gray Eagle. "I now feel my strength perfectly recovered, and I will go out with you tomorrow." For he was the most courageous and warlike of them all.

Next day they went forth together, the older brother seating himself near the lake. Peepi-geewi-zains started out, and soon pounced on a duck.

Well done! thought his brother, who saw his success. But just as he was reaching the woods with his prize, up came a large white owl from a tree, where he had been watching, and laid claim to it. He had nearly wrested the duck from Peepi-geewi-zains, when Gray Eagle came up and, fixing his talons in both sides of the owl, flew home with him.

The little pigeon hawk followed him closely and was overjoyed to think he had brought home something at last. When they had alighted, he flew in the owl's face, and wanted to tear out his eyes. "Gently," said the gray eagle. "Do not be so revengeful. This will be a lesson to him from now on not to steal from anyone who is weaker than himself." So, after giving him good advice and telling him what kind of herbs would cure his wounds, they let the owl go.

While this was taking place, and before the owl had yet got out of sight, two visitors appeared at the hollow tree. They were the two nestmates, who had just returned from the south after passing the winter there. Thus they were all happily reunited, and each one soon chose a mate and flew off into the woods.

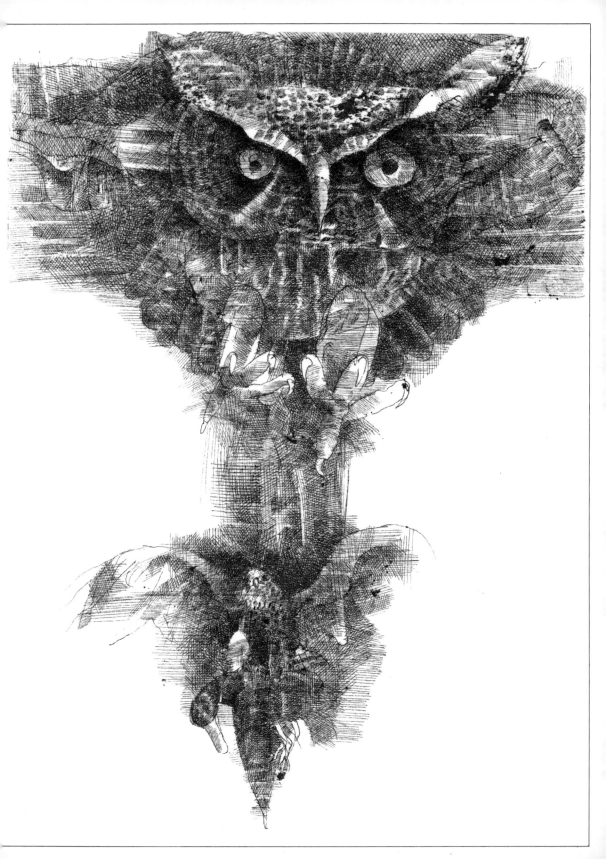

Spring had now revisited the north. The cold winds had ceased, the ice had melted, the streams were open, and the forest once again became green.

Sheem

A solitary lodge stood on the banks of a remote lake. It was near the hour of sunset. Silence reigned within and without. Not a sound was heard but the low breathing of the head of the poor family that dwelt there. Beside him stood his wife and their three children, two of whom were almost grown.

The third and youngest was a mere child.

All the family's skill in medicine had been tried, but to no effect. They moved about the lodge in whispers, awaiting the departure of the spirit. As one of the last acts of kindness, the skin door of the lodge had been thrown back to let in the fresh air. The dying man felt a momentary return of strength, and raising himself a little, addressed his family.

"I leave you in a world of hardship. It has taken all my strength to supply you with food and protect you from storms and cold. For you, my partner in life, I have less sorrow in leaving, because I know you will not remain long behind me. The time of your suffering will be shortened. But you, my children, listen to my words. Much evil dwells in the world about you. It is for your sake, as well as for mine, that I withdrew years ago from my tribe to spend my days in this lonely spot. I have contented myself with the company of your mother and yourselves during seasons of scarcity and want, while our kindred feasted in a place where food is plenty. But strife and bloodshed are with them there, while we have lived in peace. If we have sometimes suffered bodily want, we have escaped from pain of mind.

"My life is now at its close. I will shut my eyes in peace if you, my children, will promise to cherish each other. Let not your mother suffer during the few days that are left to her. And I charge you on no account to forsake your younger brother. I give you both my dying charge to keep him safe and well."

He sank exhausted on his pallet. The family waited a moment as if expecting to hear more, but when they came to his side, the spirit had taken its flight.

The mother and the daughter cried aloud in their grief. The oldest son kept his feelings within him, and remained silent. Soon, with the bow and the net, he learned the tasks his father had once performed. Time wore heavily, however. Five moons had filled and waned, and the sixth was near its full, when the mother also died. In her last moments she reminded her children of their promise to their father. Still free from selfish motives, they readily renewed the pledge.

Winter passed. Spring with its warmth and color cheered the drooping spirits of the lonely family. The girl, being the oldest, assumed the duties of a parent, expressing particular affection for the younger brother, who was somewhat sickly and delicate. The other boy soon showed signs of restlessness and ambition, and addressed his sister as follows:

"My sister, are we always to live as if there were no other human beings in the world? Must I deprive myself of the pleasure of associating with my own kind? I have found the answer for myself. I shall seek the villages of men, and you cannot prevent me."

The sister replied: "I do not say No, my brother, to what you desire. And yet we have promised to cherish each other. Nothing should be allowed to separate us, especially from our younger brother, who is but a child and unable to care for himself. If we follow our separate desires, we will surely neglect him, whom we are bound by vows, both to our father and our mother, to protect."

The young man received these words in silence. He appeared daily to grow more restless and moody, and one day, taking his bow and arrows, left the lodge and never returned.

Out of necessity the sister found within her a strength she had not known before. With renewed effort, drawing upon her knowledge of the ways of the forest, she was able to supply her younger brother's needs. For a long time she cared for him, protecting him with a mother's affection. At length, however, she began to grow weary of her charge and longed for other companionship. No one ever came to share her tasks or to converse with her in her native language. The long years, which had added to her strength and ability to direct the affairs of the household, had also brought with them the irresistible desire for society. Finally, selfishness took control of her heart. Thinking of nothing now but a change in her way of life, she lost sight of the promise she had formerly clung to with so much affection.

One day, collecting all the food she had saved for emergencies and bringing a pile of wood to the door, she said to her little brother, "You must not stray from the lodge. I am going to seek our older brother. I shall be back soon."

Taking her bundle, she set off in search of a village. She soon found one, and became so taken up with the pleasures of social life that the thought of her brother was almost entirely obliterated. In due time she accepted a proposal of marriage.

Meanwhile her older brother had also married, and lived at the edge of the same lake whose far-reaching shores contained the abandoned lodge of his father and his forsaken brother.

Now, when the sister had been gone not many days, the boy, finding himself at the end of his food, began to dig roots and pick berries, living in this manner until the earth was finally covered by snow. Winter came on with all its harshness. He was forced to leave the lodge in search of other food. Sometimes he passed the night in the clefts of old trees or in caves, and ate scraps that had been left by wolves.

Eventually the wolves became his only resource, and he grew so fearless of them that he would sit close by while they devoured their prey. They, in turn, became so familiar with his face that they were undisturbed by his approach and, appearing to sympathize with him in his forsaken condition, would always leave something for him to eat.

In this way he lived till spring. As soon as the lake was free from ice, he followed his newfound friends to the shore. That same day, as it happened, his older brother was fishing in his canoe a considerable

distance out in the lake, when he thought he heard the cries of a child on the shore. He wondered how any child could exist in such a bleak and forsaken wilderness. He listened again and distinctly heard the cry repeated. As quickly as possible he made for the shore. Approaching land, he recognized his little brother and heard him calling.

> *Neesia, neesia,*
> *Shyegwuh goosuh!*
> *Ni my een gwun iewh!*
> *Ni my een gwun iewh!*
>   *Heo hwooh.*

> (Brother! My brother!
> My fate is near!
> My woes are ended!
> I shall be changed!)

He was still more astonished when, coming up to the shore, he saw his younger brother partly changed into a wolf. He immediately leaped on shore and

tried to catch him in his arms, crying, "*Nee sheema!
Nee sheema!*" ("My little brother! My little brother!")
But the boy eluded his grasp, howling as he fled.

In anguish and with redoubled force, the older
brother cried out again, *"Nee sheema! Nee sheema!
Nee sheema!"*

But the nearer he approached, the more rapidly
the transformation progressed, the boy alternately
howling and calling out the name, first of his brother,
then of his sister, until the change was completely
accomplished, whereupon he exclaimed, "I am a
wolf!" and bounded out of sight.

The Fire Plume

The season had begun when fish are plenty near the
shore of the lake. Wassamo, setting out early in his
canoe, had made his way along the shore to a fishing
ground, where he had spread his nets. It was evening now, and as he pulled in the nets he saw that

he was fortunate, for here and there the meshes were white with fish.

Immediately he set a kettle on his campfire, and soon the fish were boiling. When they were done, he removed the kettle, and taking a wooden ladle, skimmed off the oil, for the fish were very fat. He had a torch of twisted bark in one hand to give light, but when it came time to remove the fish he did not know how to hold it.

Taking off his leg bands, he wrapped them around his head and tied up the lighted torch so that it rose from his forehead in a feather of flames. With both hands free he began to take out the fish, every now and then moving his head as he blew off the oil from the broth. As he hastened to remove the last of them, blowing repeatedly over the kettle, the plume of fire above his head waved brilliantly in the air.

Suddenly he heard a laugh. Looking out as far as the torch threw light, he saw two beautiful young women smiling at him. Charmed by their appearance, he started toward them. But just as he was about to speak, he fell unconscious, and both he and they vanished together.

Recovering his senses, he found himself in a superb lodge extending as far as the eye could see. Someone spoke to him, saying, "Stranger, awake, and take something to eat." He arose and sat up. On each side of the lodge there were rows of people sitting in regular order. At a distance he could see two prominent persons who looked older than the rest and who appeared to command obedience from all around them. They were the Old Spirit and his wife.

The Old Spirit addressed him, saying, "Son, my daughters brought you here. They saw you at the fishing ground. When you tried to approach them, you fell unconscious, and they brought you underground to this place.

"I have often wished to have one of your people

live with us. If you can make up your mind to remain, I will give you one of my daughters in marriage." Wassamo dropped his head and made no
answer. By his silence he gave his assent.

"All of your wants shall be supplied," said the
Old Spirit. "Here is my daughter. Take her, she
shall be your wife." And from that time on they
sat beside each other in the lodge and were considered as married.

Then the wife of the Old Spirit spoke and said,
"Daughter, your husband cannot eat what we eat.
You must get him what he is accustomed to."

In reply the daughter pushed her hand through
the side of the lodge and took a white fish out of
the lake. Every day from that time on she used the
same method, giving her husband trout, pike, stur-
geon, or whatever kind of fish he desired. Likewise
she would give him the meat of any animal or fowl.
For animals walked over the roof of the lodge,
birds sat upon its poles, and the waters came so near

to its side that the spirits had only to reach outside for whatever they wished.

One day the Old Spirit said, "Son-in-law, I am in want of tobacco. You shall return to visit your parents and make known my wishes. The distance is short to your village. A path leads directly to it, and when you get there, do not forget my request."

Wassamo promised to do as he was told and soon set out, together with his wife. They followed a path to the top of a rise, then walked a short distance under the lake, emerging from the water at a point not far from the village.

When they arrived, the people were thrown into a state of commotion. All were anxious to see Wassamo, for they had thought him dead. While the excitement was at its height, he entered the lodge of his parents. They were filled with joy to see him. He related all that had happened to him, how he had attached the fire plume to his head and how he had disappeared from the campsite. He told them where he had been and how he had come to be married. They were astonished at his wife's beauty, and more so at her ability to converse with them in their own language.

All was joy in the village. There was nothing but feasting. People came from nearby villages to offer them welcome and to present their tobacco to the Old Spirit's daughter and her husband. In return they asked that the spirits grant them long life, success in hunting, and a plentiful supply of food. Wassamo promised to convey each of their requests to his father-in-law.

So much tobacco had been offered that it filled two sacks made of moose skin. On the outside of these skins each person painted his own family mark, or totem, to show who had given the tobacco.

When the time came for Wassamo and his wife to leave, he told his relatives not to follow them or see how they disappeared. Taking the tobacco, they said good-bye to all—all but one cousin who had been Wassamo's closest companion. He insisted on going with them a distance, and when they got to the edge of the lake, he urged them to take him with them. Wassamo told him it was impossible, that it was only spirits who could grant the power to make such a journey. With great affection, then, they parted. The cousin watched as they walked into the water. He returned home and told his family and friends that he had witnessed their disappearance.

When Wassamo and his wife reached their home under the lake, the Old Spirit greeted them with open arms. They presented him with the tobacco and told him all the requests of the people above. He promised he would attend to them all, but before he could do so he must first invite the other spirits to come share the tobacco and smoke with him.

The great coming together of the spirits was

promptly arranged, and toward the middle of the day they began to arrive. There were spirits from all parts of the country, some good, some wicked, some dangerous. Suddenly, when most had arrived, Wassamo heard the roaring and foaming of waters. Rushing in, they passed through the lodge like a raging storm. Tremendous pieces of rocks, whole trees, logs, and stumps rolled past and were swept away in the current. The spirit of waterfalls had arrived.

Next they heard the roaring of waves as if beating against a rocky shore. In a few moments the waves of the lake rolled into the lodge, mountain-high and covered with silver-sparkling foam. Wassamo felt their pressure and with difficulty clung to his seat, for each one seemed as if it would overwhelm him. This was the spirit of the islands in the surrounding lake.

At last all of the spirits were gathered, including the guardian spirit of Wassamo's tribe. The Old

Spirit arose and addressed the assembly.

"Brothers," he said, "I have invited you to share with me this offering made by the mortals on earth, which has been brought to us by my son-in-law. Brothers, you see their wishes and desires." And he pointed to the totems covering the tobacco-filled moose skins.

"Brothers," he continued, "the offering is worthy of our consideration. Brothers, I see nothing on my part to prevent our granting their requests. They do not appear to be unreasonable. One thing more I would say—brothers, it is this. My son-in-law is a mortal. I wish to keep him with me, and it is in our power to make him one of us."

"*Hoke! Hoke!*" ran through the whole company of spirits. Thus they signified their approval. The tobacco was then divided equally among them. They would grant the requests of the people on earth and also the request of the Old Spirit regarding his son-in-law.

When the company had left, the Old Spirit told Wassamo that he must once more visit his parents and relatives. "It is merely to tell them that their wishes are granted and then to bid them farewell forever."

Shortly thereafter, Wassamo and his wife set out once again, bringing with them the message that the people's requests for long life, good hunting, and plentiful food had been granted. "Now," said Wassamo, "I must bid you all farewell."

His parents and friends raised their voices in loud lamentation. They went with him to the edge of the lake, where they all seated themselves to see him make his final departure. The day was mild, the sky clear. Not a cloud appeared, nor a breath of wind to disturb the bright surface of the lake. The most perfect silence reigned throughout the company. They gazed intently on Wassamo and his wife as they waded out into the water, waving their hands. They saw them go into deeper and deeper water.

They saw the waves close over their heads. All at once they raised a loud and piercing wail. They looked again. A red glow as if the sun had glanced on a wave, marked the spot for an instant, but the feather of flames and his wife had disappeared forever.

INDIAN TERMS

*(Terms sufficiently explained
in the text are not included here.)*

AISSIBUN (ess–see–BUN): raccoon.

HOMINY: a whitish food, made by boiling bits of corn.

MANABOZHO: name of a mythical hero.

MISKODEED: Spring Beauty, a common wildflower of eastern North America.

ODJIBWA (oh–JIB–way): name meaning puckered moccasin, a type of moccasin with a gathered seam, worn by the Chippewas. (Note: *Chippewa* is a variation of the name *Odjibwa*.)

PEBOAN (peb–BONE): winter.

PEMMICAN: a concentrated food made of dried meat shreds mixed with fat.

SEEGWUN (see–GWUN): spring.

SHEEM: shortened form of *nee sheema*, meaning "my little brother."

SHINGOUB (Shing–GOOB): spruce.

TOTEM: a sign or symbolic picture, usually representing an animal, used as a family mark.

WAMPUM: beads of white and purple shell, highly valued and often used as money.

WASSAMO: name meaning plume or feather of fire.